D0227790

Wild
Wilf

by Jenny Jinks   illustrated by
                        Patricia Pessoa

Wilf wanted to live in the wild.

He took his bag...

...and his ted...

...and left.

Wilf liked the wild.

He swung in the trees.

"Whee!"

He sprang from branch to branch.

"Aaaaaaah!"

Wilf missed the branch.

CRASH!

He fell down.

When Wilf was hungry, he ate
nuts from the trees...

...and bugs from under a log.

But the nuts were hard.

CRUNCH!

And the bugs were wriggly.

"Yuck!"

When Wilf was mucky, he and Ted
had a bath in a pond.

But he was still mucky.

And he began to smell too.

Wilf had a stick to keep the
big hairy spiders away.

It did not work.

"Get off!"

Wilf made a den from some branches.

It was a bit small.

The den was not very good
when it was wet.

Or cold.

Or windy.

When it got dark, Wilf made shadow puppets with his torch to cheer Ted up.

But Wilf's torch went out.

"Uh-oh..."

It was dark.

Very dark.

Wilf was cold and wet.

Wilf was dirty and smelly.

Wilf was hungry.

Wilf liked living in the wild... for a bit.

"Wilf! Dinner!"

But he liked going home
even better.

Quiz

1. Wilf wanted to live...
a) Indoors
b) In a tree house
c) In the wild

2. What did Wilf try to eat?
a) Seeds and plants
b) Berries and nuts
c) Nuts and bugs

3. Where did Wilf have a bath?
a) In a pond
b) In a bathtub
c) In a puddle

4. What did Wilf use to make a den?

a) Leaves

b) Branches

c) Ted

5. What did Wilf's mum shout?

a) Wilf! Come here!

b) Wilf! Dinner!

c) Bed time!

Turn over for answers

Book Bands for Guided Reading

The Institute of Education book banding system is a scale of colours that reflects the various levels of reading difficulty. The bands are assigned by taking into account the content, the language style, the layout and phonics. Word, phrase and sentence level work is also taken into consideration.

Maverick Early Readers are a bright, attractive range of books covering the pink to white bands. All of these books have been book banded for guided reading to the industry standard and edited by a leading educational consultant.

To view the whole Maverick Readers scheme, visit our website at
www.maverickearlyreaders.com

Or scan the QR code above to view our scheme instantly!

Quiz Answers: 1c, 2c, 3a, 4b, 5b